Working With Sounds Phonics
Book 1

Zehra Shervani
Neera Taneja
(Modern School, New Delhi)

Published by
STERLING PRESS PRIVATE LIMITED
A-59, Okhla Industrial Area, Phase-II
(D-26) (I.P.S.) New Delhi-110 020
e-mail: ghai.sterlingpub@gmail.com
Website: www.sterlingpublishers.com

© 2001 Sterling Press Private Limited
Reprint 2002, 2003, 2008

🛉 sterling

STERLING PRESS PRIVATE LIMITED

Published by
STERLING PRESS PRIVATE LIMITED
A-59, Okhla Industrial Area, Phase - II, New Delhi-20
Tel: 26386165; Fax: 91-11-26383788
E-mail: ghai@nde.vsnl.net.in
Website: www.sterlingpublishers.com

Printed at Sterling Publishers Pvt. Ltd., New Delhi-110020.

Author's Note

This series focusses on all the major aspects of letter-sound relationships. It deals with the 40+ sounds of English, besides the alphabet sounds. There are initial and final consonant sounds, short and long vowel sounds, blends and digraphs.

Through games and activities children are provided with ample opportunities to become familiar with common letter patterns. At the same time they can practise writing these patterns in a well formed style. The children first "look" at the familiar letter patterns before they write them.

'Rainbow' writing in which the letter is traced over in four different colours helps to reinforce the words/letters as units of sound.

'Tracking' exercises help to improve eye-hand coordination, as the children keep the pencil on the paper while they track from left to right along a line. They will loop particular letters/words as they come to them. These are embedded between carefully chosen distractors.

<u>eg.</u>   ⓐ   b   ⓐ   ⓐ   c   a   d   a   e

Writing the letters large on the black board and 'finger' writing on contrasting surfaces like sandpaper, carpet etc. have been found to be useful. FLASH CARDS can also be used to bring in variety and keep up the interest.

Each book supports the work done in the previous book.

Contents

VOWELS

Say the sound of the first letter of each picture and 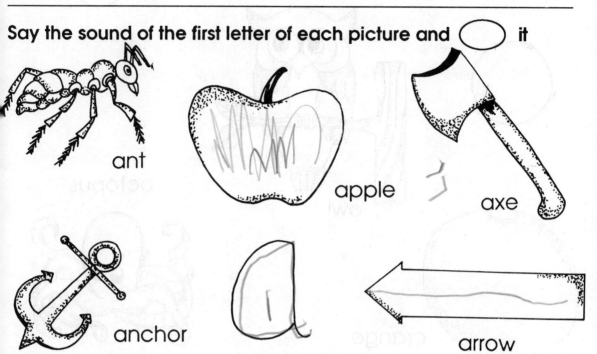 it

ant

apple

axe

anchor

arrow

in

igloo

insect

ink

5

Say the sound of the first letter of each picture and 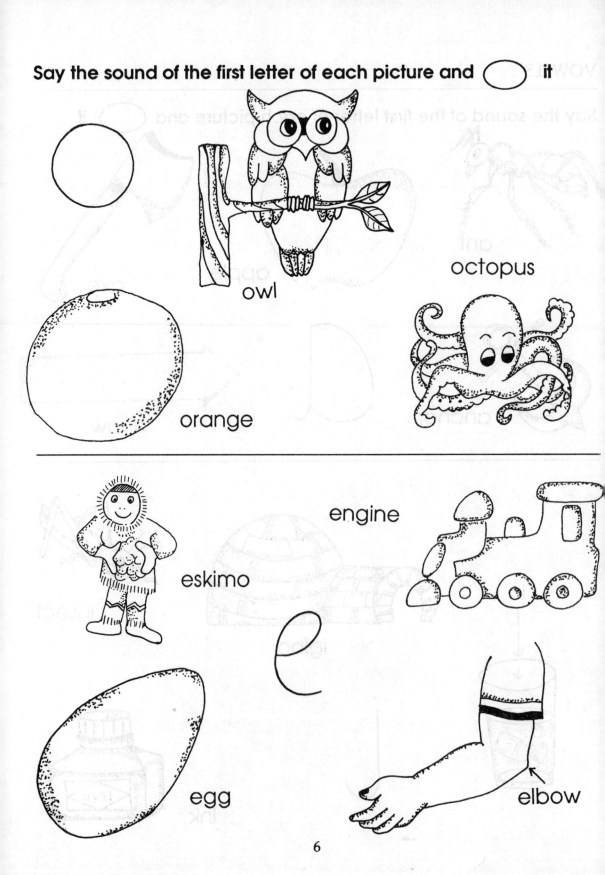 **it**

owl

octopus

orange

eskimo

engine

egg

elbow

6

the first letter of each picture and say its sound

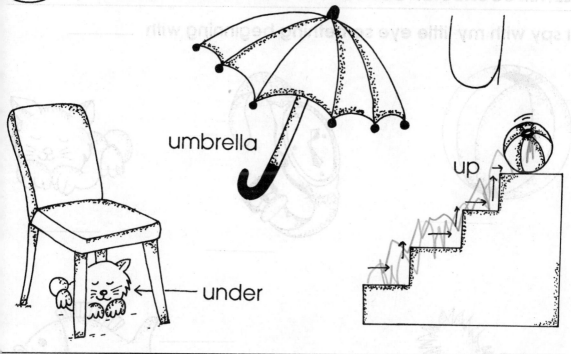

umbrella

under

up →

THE VOWELS

a b c d e f g h i j k l m n o p q r s t u v w x y z

a	e		i		o		u
a	b	a	c	e	d	e	f	u
h	i	i	j	k	o	u	l	m
i	z	e	n	a	p	e	q	u
i	a	s	e	t	i	o	w	u
a	v	e	z	i	o	x	u	y

LETTER SOUNDS OF CONSONANTS

I spy with my little eye something beginning with ———

LETTER SOUNDS OF CONSONANTS

I spy with my little eye something beginning with _____

Trace over | at | **with four different colours**

Track at

at	at	at	at	ta	ta	ut
ta	at	at	ut	ta	ot	tu
at	ut	at	at	at	ta	at
at	ta	ot	at	at	at	ta

Read and write. Colour the pictures.

cat
c _ _
c _ _ t

nat
h _ _
h _ _ t

mat
m _ _
m _ _ t

rat
r _ _
r _ _ t

Read	Copy	√ the correct picture	
bat	— — —		
cat	— — —		
hat	— — —		
mat	— — —		
rat	— — —		

◯ **the twins**

1.	bat	cat	bat	fat
2.	rat	rat	hat	mat
3.	hat	cat	fat	hat
4.	sat	rat	sat	mat

Write 'at' words on the mat

b ____   c ____   h ____

f ____   s ____   r ____

Trace over `an` **with four different colours**

Track `an`

an	na	an	an	na	an	an
an	un	an	on	an	an	en
an	na	no	an	an	an	an
on	no	an	na	an	an	an

Read and write. Colour the pictures.

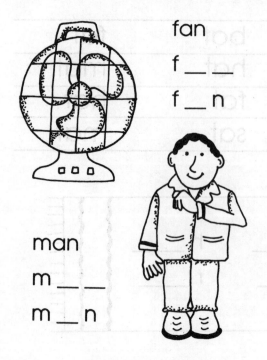

fan

f _ _

f _ n

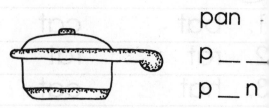

pan

p _ _

p _ n

man

m _ _

m _ n

van

v _ _

v _ n

12

SPELL AND WRITE

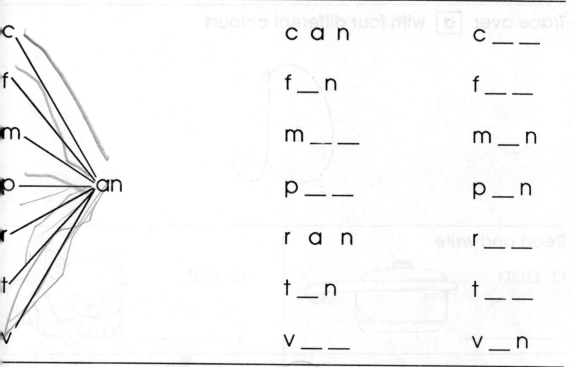

c a n	c _ _
f _ n	f _ _
m _ _	m _ n
p _ _	p _ n
r a n	r _ _
t _ n	t _ _
v _ _	v _ n

Write [an] words on the <u>van</u>. Colour the <u>van's</u> wheels.

13

SIGHT WORD

Trace over [a] with four different colours

Read and write

a pan

_____

a cat

_____

a van

_____

a bat

_____

a fan

_____

a rat

_____

a man

_____

a hat

_____

14

SIGHT WORD

Trace over `and` **with four different colours**

Fill in the gaps

1. a [cat image] and a [mouse image]

1. a   cat   and   a   rat

2. a [pin image] _____ a [pan image]

2. _____

3. a [van image] _____ a [can image]

3. _____

4. a [mat image] _____ a [hat image]

4. _____

Trace over ap with four colours

Track ap

ap	pa	ap	ap	ap	pa
ap	ap	op	ep	ap	ap
ap	up	ap	ap	pa	ap
ap	ap	ep	pa	ap	ap

Read and write

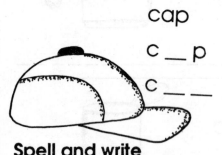

cap

c _ p

c _ _

 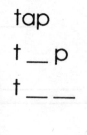

tap

t _ p

t _ _

map

m _ p

m _ _

Spell and write

l

g — ap

s

n

l _____   _____

g _____   _____

s _____   _____

n _____   _____

16

◯ the ⬚ap⬚ words and write them on the ladder.

cap   cat

   gap   ran

     lap

man   nap

    pan

       sap

map

   tap   sat

rat

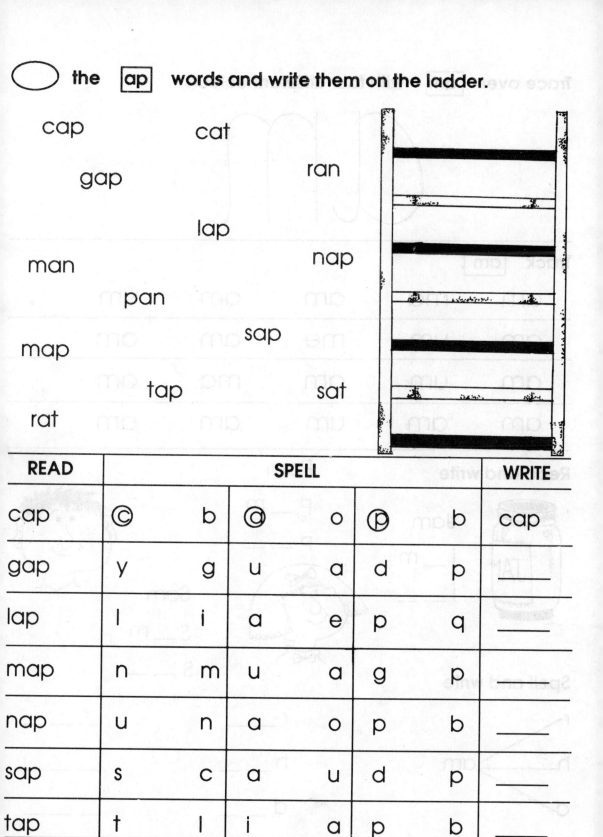

READ	SPELL					WRITE
cap	©c	b	@a	o	℗p	b	cap
gap	y	g	u	a	d	p	____
lap	l	i	a	e	p	q	____
map	n	m	u	a	g	p	____
nap	u	n	a	o	p	b	____
sap	s	c	a	u	d	p	____
tap	t	l	i	a	p	b	____

17

Trace over am **with four different colours**

Track am

am	ma	am	am	um
am	um	me	am	am
am	um	am	ma	am
am	am	um	am	am

Read and write

Jam

j __ m

j __ __

Pam

P __ m

P __ __

Sam

S __ m

S __ __

Spell and write

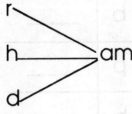

r __ __

h __ __

d __ __

__ __ __

__ __ __

__ __ __

18

READ	SPELL				WRITE
Pam	(P)	B	(am)	ma	P a m
Sam	S	C	um	am	_ _ _
ham	n	h	am	om	_ _ _
ram	m	r	om	am	_ _ _
jam	y	j	um	am	_ _ _
dam	b	d	em	am	_ _ _

Fill the **with** am **words**

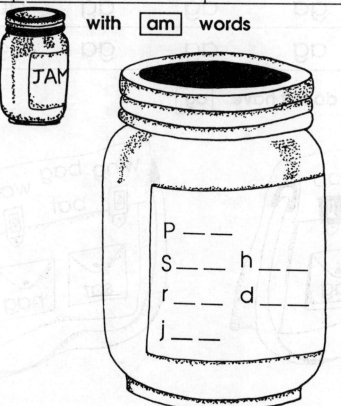

P _ _
S _ _   h _ _ _
r _ _ _   d _ _ _
j _ _

Trace over `ag` **with four different colours**

Track `ag`

ag	ga	ag	ag	ag
ag	ug	og	ag	ag
ag	ga	ag	ag	ga
ug	ag	ag	ga	og

X the words that do not have `ag`

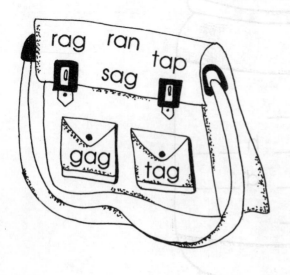

rag ran
tap
sag
gag tag

wing bag wag
bat
sat hag

READ	SPELL				WRITE
bag	ⓑ	d	ja	(ag)	b a g
gag	g	y	ag	go	_ _ _
hag	n	h	ya	ag	_ _ _
rag	r	m	ag	ay	_ _ _
sag	c	s	gu	ag	_ _ _
tag	t	l	ag	og	_ _ _
wag	v	w	ug	ag	_ _ _

WORD SEARCH

(bag)   ban   ag   rat   bag ✓

ag   ap   pen   gag

gag   hag

rag   sat   hag   rag

tan   an   wag   sag

tag   tag

sag   at   zig   ad   wag

Trace over ad **with four different colours**

ad

Track ad

ad	ad	da	ad	ad	ad
ad	ob	ub	ad	ab	ad
ad	da	ba	ab	ad	ad
ad	ad	ba	da	ab	ad

Look	Say	Cover and Write			Check ✓ or X
bad	bad	b	a	d	✓
Dad	Dad	—	—	—	
fad	fad	—	—	—	
had	had	—	—	—	
mad	mad	—	—	—	
pad	pad	—	—	—	
sad	sad	—	—	—	

22

WORD SEARCH

bad (circled)   pat   bad ✓

hat   had   fan   dad

dad   pan   had

mat   mad   sad   sad

pad   bat   lad   mad

pad

lad

Write [ad] **words on the** <u>pad</u>

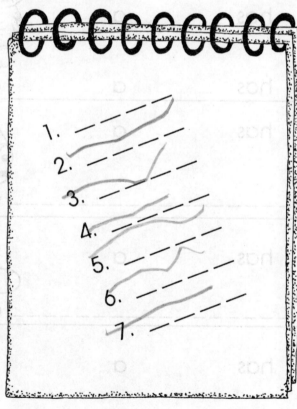

1. _ _ _ _
2. _ _ _ _
3. _ _ _ _
4. _ _ _ _
5. _ _ _ _
6. _ _ _ _
7. _ _ _ _

23

SIGHT WORD
Trace over │has│ with four different colours.

A sentence starts with a capital letter and ends with a full stop.

Fill in the gaps and copy the sentence.

Pam	has	a	cat.
Dad_____	has	a	van.
Sam_____	has	a	cap.
Pat_____	has	a	bag.

SIGHT WORD

Trace over [id] with four different colours

Trace over [have] with four different colours.

Fill in the gaps and copy the sentence

1. Pam   and   Sam   have   a

1. _____

2. Dad   and   Pam   _____

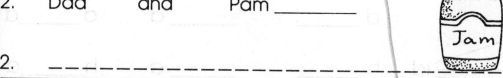

2. _____

3. Sam   and   Pat ____ a

3. _____

4. Pam   and   Dad _____ a

4. _____

Trace over │id│ **with four different colours**

id

Track │id│

id	di	id	ed	id	id
id	id	ad	id	di	id
ii	ai	id	id	id	id
id	id	di	id	id	id

Spell and Write

d_____   d _____   _____d   d_____d

h_____id h _____   _____d   h_____d

l_____   l _____   _____d   l_____d

◯ **the twins**

1.	did	dot	did	bin
2.	hid	hat	hip	hid
3.	lid	lid	lap	lot
4.	kid	hot	hat	kid

Trace over [ig] **with four different colours**

Track [ig]

ig	gi	ag	ga	ig	ig
ig	ig	ig	ag	gi	og
gi	ig	ig	ig	ga	ag
gi	ig	ag	ig	ig	ig

Read	Spell					Write
fig	ⓕ	p	ⓘ	u	y	ⓖ	f i g
dig	b	d	e	i	j	g	_ _ _
big	b	d	i	u	g	q	_ _ _
jig	l	j	a	i	y	g	_ _ _
pig	p	q	i	l	g	j	_ _ _
wig	v	w	j	i	q	g	_ _ _

27

Trace over [it] **with four different colours**

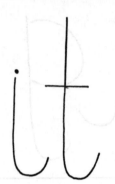

Track [it]

it	ti	it	it	at	it
it	it	il	li	it	ut
it	ut	it	li	it	il
it	it	ut	it	ta	at

Spell and Write

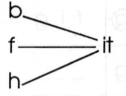

b___   b __ t
f___   f __ t
h___   h __ t

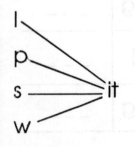

l___   l __ t
p___   p __ t
s___   s __ t
w___   w __ t

28

◯ **the twins**

1.	(bit)	bat	bag	(bit)
2.	fit	fit	fan	fat
3.	hit	hat	hit	hag
4.	lit	lap	lad	lit
5.	pit	pan	pat	pit
6.	sit	sat	sit	sad
7.	wit	wit	pat	nap

Unscramble the words and write them in the blanks.

1. fti   _ _ _   2. tbi   _ _ _

3. hti   _ _ _   4. itp   _ _ _

5. ilt   _ _ _   6. iwt   _ _ _

Write the | it | words in the <u>bit</u>.

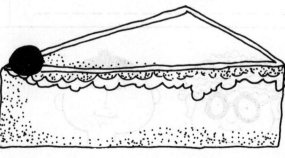

29

Trace over `im` **with four different colours**

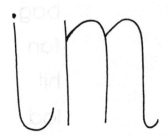

Read	Spell			Write
Jim	Ⓙ L	ⓘ u	ⓜ n	J i m
dim	b d	e i	u m	_ _ _
Tim	T F	i o	w m	_ _ _
him	h n	e i	m v	_ _ _

Fill in 'im' to complete the words and then copy the sentence.
A name always starts with a capital letter.

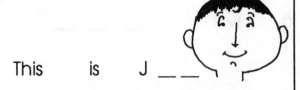

This   is   J _ _

_ _ _ _ _ _ _ _ _ _

This   is   T_ _

_ _ _ _ _ _ _ _ _

T _ _ is J _ _'s friend

_ _ _ _ _ _ _ _ _ _ _ _

SIGHT WORD

Trace over his **with four different colours**

Sort the words and write the sentence

1. name   is   His   Tim

_ _

2. is   bag   This   his

_ _

3. his   is   shirt   This

_ _

4. are   shoes   These   his

_ _

31

Trace over ip **with four different colours**

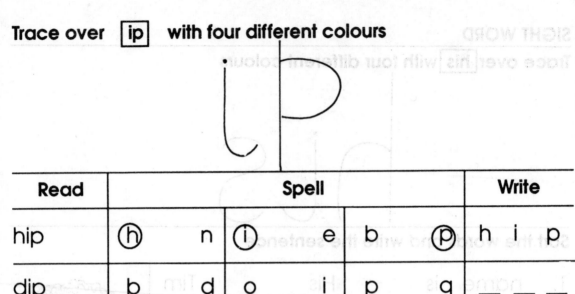

Read	Spell							Write
hip	ⓗ	n	ⓘ	e	b		ⓟ	h i p
dip	b	d	o	i	p		q	_ _ _
lip	l	j	i	u	d		p	_ _ _
rip	m	r	a	i	g		p	_ _ _
tip	t	y	i	u	p		d	_ _ _
nip	u	n	j	i	b		p	_ _ _
pip	p	q	i	l	p		q	_ _ _

Draw a line and match the words

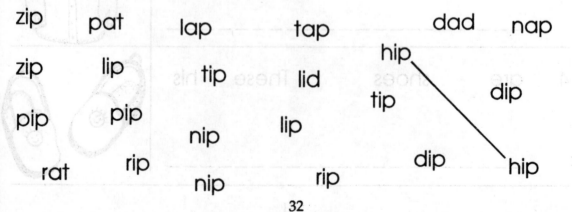

zip   pat   lap ——— tap   dad   nap

zip   lip   tip   lid   hip   dip

pip   pip   nip   lip   tip

rat   rip   nip   rip   dip   hip

Trace over ix **with four different colours**

Spell and write

f
m —— ix
s

f _ _   _ _ x   f _ x
m _ _   _ _ x   m _ x
s _ _   _ _ x   s _ x

Sort the words and write the sentence

1.   can   a   fan   Tim   fix

_ _

2.   six   has   Jim   pins

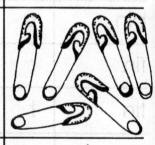

_ _

3.   to this Pam mix can cake a bake

_ _

Trace over in **with four different colours**

Track in

in	ni	in	an	on	in
in	an	in	in	ni	im
in	in	in	ni	ni	un
in	in	ii	nn	in	in

Read	Spell						Write		
pin	(p)	q	o	(i)	(n)	m	p	i	n
bin	c	b	i	o	d	n	_	_	_
fin	r	f	u	i	n	s	_	_	_
tin	t	s	i	t	r	n	_	_	_
din	b	d	i	j	n	s	_	_	_
sin	s	p	l	i	n	t	_	_	_
win	q	w	k	i	m	n	_	_	_

34

SIGHT WORD
Trace over ⬚is⬚ **with four different colours**

A question begins with a capital letter and ends with a '?' mark.

Read the question and copy it.

1. Is   this   a   cat ?

    _

2. Is   this   a   hut ?

    _

3. Is   this   a   pen ?

    _

4. Is   this   a   van ?

    _

SIGHT WORD

Trace over | this | **with four colours**

A sentence begins with a capital letter and ends with a full stop.

Fill in the blanks and read. Then copy the sentence.

| 1. | | This   is   a   cat. |
| | | ------------------------------------- |

| 2. | | _____   is   a   z_____. |
| | | ------------------------------------- |

| 3. | | _____   is   a   p_____. |
| | | ------------------------------------- |

| 4. | | _____   is   a   v_____. |
| | | ------------------------------------- |

Trace over is **and** was **with four different colours**

Look at the pictures and fill in 'is'/'was' to complete the sentence. Then copy the sentence.

	The water _____ in the glass
	1. _ _ _ _ _ _ _ _ _ _ _ _ _ _
The water _____ in the glass	
2. _ _ _ _ _ _ _ _ _ _ _ _ _	
	It _____ raining
	3. _ _ _ _ _ _ _ _ _ _ _ _
It _____ raining	
4. _ _ _ _ _ _ _ _ _ _ _ _ _	

X the odd one out

(it)	pit	bit	fit	fat
(ig)	big	bag	fig	dig
(id)	did	hid	hat	lid
(ip)	zip	ran	hip	lip
(ix)	six	mix	man	fix
(im)	him	rag	dim	rim
(in)	win	wag	sin	tin

Fill in the blanks with the right word. Then copy the sentence.

1. Joe is a _____ (fit/fat) boy.

2. This is a _____ (big/bag) hat.

3. The cat _____ (ran/hid) after the rat.

4. Tim _____ (sat/bat) in the van.

5. These are _____ (mix/six) balls.

Trace over `ot` **with four different colours**

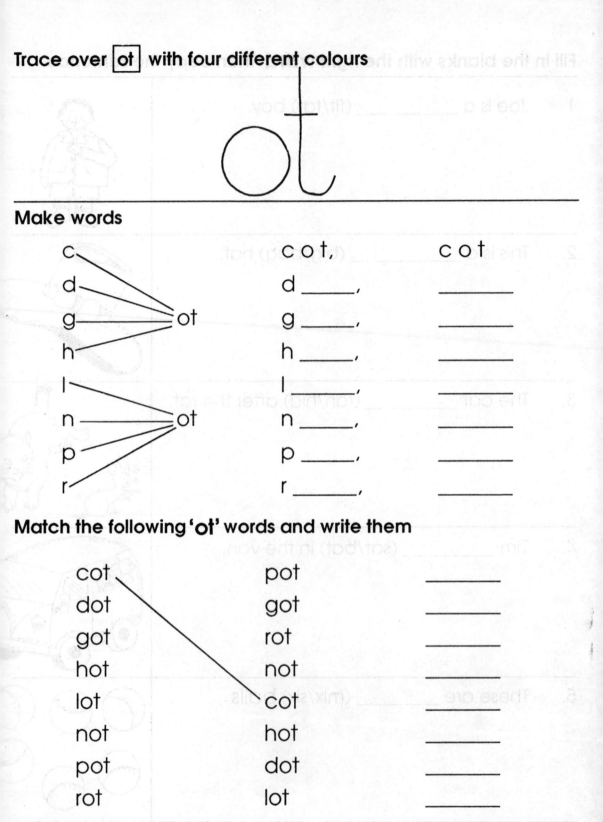

Make words

c		c o t,		c o t
d		d ____,		_____
g	ot	g ____,		_____
h		h ____,		_____
l		l ____,		_____
n	ot	n ____,		_____
p		p ____,		_____
r		r _____,		_____

Match the following 'ot' words and write them

cot	pot	_____
dot	got	_____
got	rot	_____
hot	not	_____
lot	cot	_____
not	hot	_____
pot	dot	_____
rot	lot	_____

40

Track ot

ot	at	ot	et	am	ot
et	ot	ot	at	et	it
ut	at	it	ot	ot	et
it	at	ot	ot	it	ot
ot	et	ot	at	ot	it

X the odd one out

hot	hot	hat	hot	hot
dot	bat	dot	dot	dot
got	jam	got	got	got
cot	cot	cot	cat	cot
rot	rot	rat	rot	rot

How many ot words can you fit in the pots?

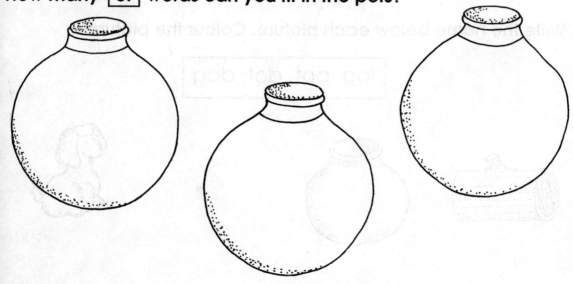

Trace over og **with four different colours**

Fill in the blanks to make og **words**

bog,	bog,	bog,	bog,
cog	co __,	c ____,	
dog,	do __,	d ____,	_____
fog,	fo __,	f ____,	_____
hog,	ho __,	h ____,	_____
jog,	jo __,	j ____,	_____
log,	lo __,	l ____,	_____

Write the name below each picture. Colour the pictures.

log, pot, dot, dog

_____ _____ _____ _____

42

Read	Spell and circle						Write
bog	(b)	d	a	(o)	y	(g)	bog
cog	r	c	o	a	g	p	
dog	b	d	u	o	y	g	
log	l	t	o	e	g	p	
fog	t	f	o	a	g	p	
hog	h	l	i	o	q	g	
jog	j	y	o	u	j	g	

Track og

og	at	og	am	at	og
eg	og	at	op	og	og
og	an	am	og	op	og
ug	og	og	op	at	on

How many 'og' words can you fit in the log?

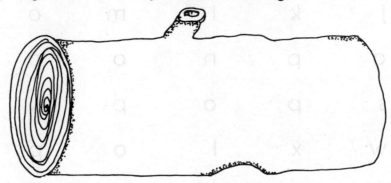

43

Trace over op with four different colours

Make words

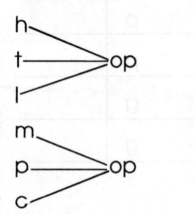

h____ op   h<u>op</u>,   <u>hop</u>

t____ op   t ____,   _____

l   l ____,   _____

m   m____,   _____

p____ op   p____,   _____

c   c____,   _____

Word Search

hop, top, lop, mop, ~~cop~~, pop

a	b	c	h	o	p	d
e	c	o	p	f	g	h
i	j	k	l	m	o	p
t	o	p	n	o	p	q
r	s	p	o	p	r	u
v	w	x	l	o	p	y

44

Circle the twins

(hop)	top	mop	(hop)
mop	lop	hop	lop
top	hop	cop	cop
top	mop	top	pop
pop	mop	cop	mop

Track [op]

op	at	am	op	an
op	ap	op	op	ot
am	op	at	op	am
op	ap	op	ot	op
ap	at	op	op	og

Match the picture to the word. Colour the pictures.

mop

top,   hop,

45

Trace over od **with four different colours**

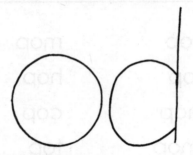

Fill in the blanks with od **Then read the words.**

cod, G___, n___ p___, r___,

Match the following 'od' words and write them

cod	rod	_____
God	nod	_____
mod	pod	_____
nod	God	_____
pod	cod	_____
rod	mod	_____

Read the words in the balls. Colour those parts of the balls that have rhyming words.

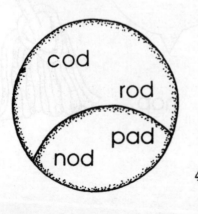

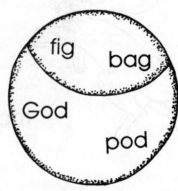

46

Track od

od	od	ad	od	od	am
od	on	am	ot	od	od
ud	od	at	od	ot	op
od	ot	od	od	at	og
eg	od	og	od	at	od

X the odd one out

rod	cod	bat	pod
pod	nod	Tod	tap
mod	mad	cod	nod
man	mod	God	cod
Tod	nod	pod	mat

Write the name of the picture. Colour the pictures.

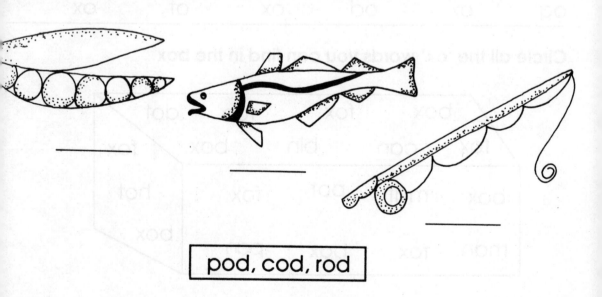

_____

_____

_____

pod, cod, rod

47

Trace over ox with four different colours

Fill in the blanks and colour

b o x

b __ x

__ o x

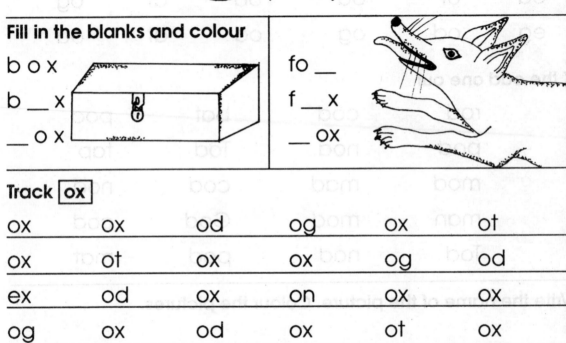

fo __

f __ x

__ ox

Track ox

ox	ox	od	og	ox	ot
ox	ot	ox	ox	og	od
ex	od	ox	on	ox	ox
og	ox	od	ox	ot	ox

Circle all the 'ox' words you can find in the box

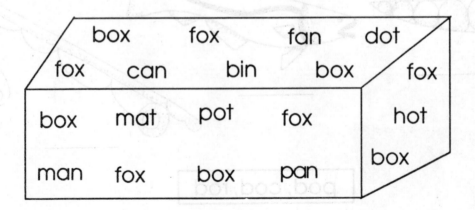

box   fox   fan   dot

fox   can   bin   box   fox

box   mat   pot   fox   hot

man   fox   box   pan   box

Put these words in the right column

hot, top, fog, mod, dog, dot, pod, hop

ot	op	og	od

Circle the name of the picture and colour

hot	hot
top	pot

dog	mod
hog	pod

mop	jog
cop	rod

log	box
cog	fox

Trace over for **with four colours**

for

Fill in for **in the box and colour**

This bat is for Tod.	This top is [ ] Pam.
This dog is [ ] Tom.	This rod is [ ] Pop.

Fill in the blanks with 'for' and copy the sentences. Remember a sentence starts with a capital letter and ends with a fullstop.

This   cot   is   <u>for</u>   Pam.

<u>This</u>   <u>cot</u>   <u>is</u>   <u>for</u>   <u>Pam</u>.

This   dog   is _____   Tom.

_ _ _ _ _ _ _ _ _ _ _ _ _ _ _ _ _.

This   mop   is _____   Mom.

_ _ _ _ _ _ _ _ _ _ _ _ _ _ _ _ _.

50

Trace over on with four different colours

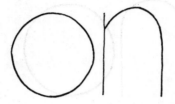

Fill in on in the box and colour the picture

A rat is ☐ a mat.

A cat is ☐ a hat.

A dog sat ☐ a log.

A bird is ☐ a pen.

X the odd one out

on	on	on	in	on
on	on	an	on	on
on	un	on	on	on
on	on	on	on	in
on	on	on	on	on

51

Trace over no with four different colours

Fill in the blanks to make 'no'

n o,   __ o,   ____

__ o,   ____,   n __

Track no

on	no	on	un	no	no
no	an	no	no	on	in
on	no	an	no	in	no
no	no	no	on	on	no

Write no on the blank bricks of the wall

◯ all the 'no's you can find on the mats

no   no   no

no   no   in   no   un

to   no   on   no   no   no

52

Trace over go **and** to **with four different colours**

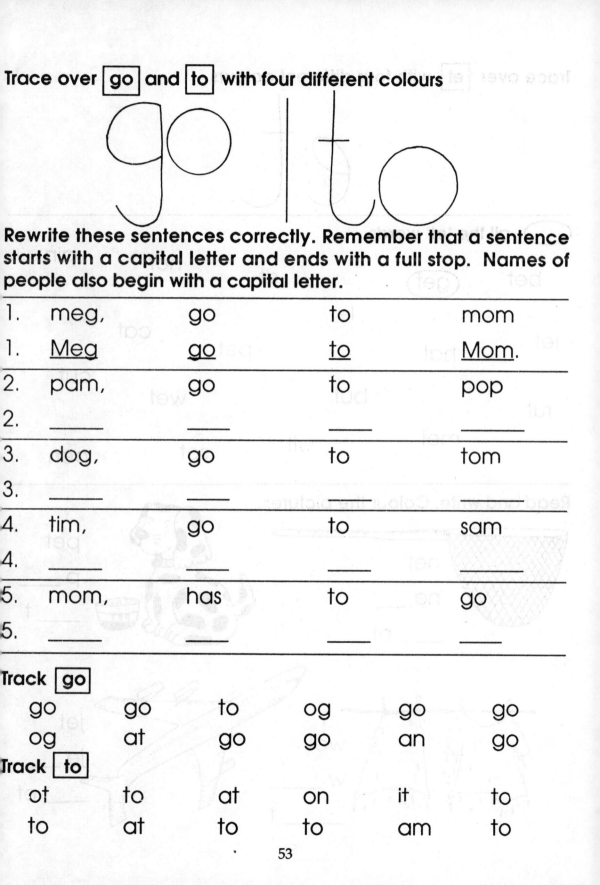

Rewrite these sentences correctly. Remember that a sentence starts with a capital letter and ends with a full stop. Names of people also begin with a capital letter.

1.	meg,	go	to	mom
1.	<u>Meg</u>	<u>go</u>	<u>to</u>	<u>Mom</u>.
2.	pam,	go	to	pop
2.	___	___	___	___
3.	dog,	go	to	tom
3.	___	___	___	___
4.	tim,	go	to	sam
4.	___	___	___	___
5.	mom,	has	to	go
5.	___	___	___	___

Track go

go	go	to	og	go	go
og	at	go	go	an	go

Track to

ot	to	at	on	it	to
to	at	to	to	am	to

Trace over et **with four different colours**

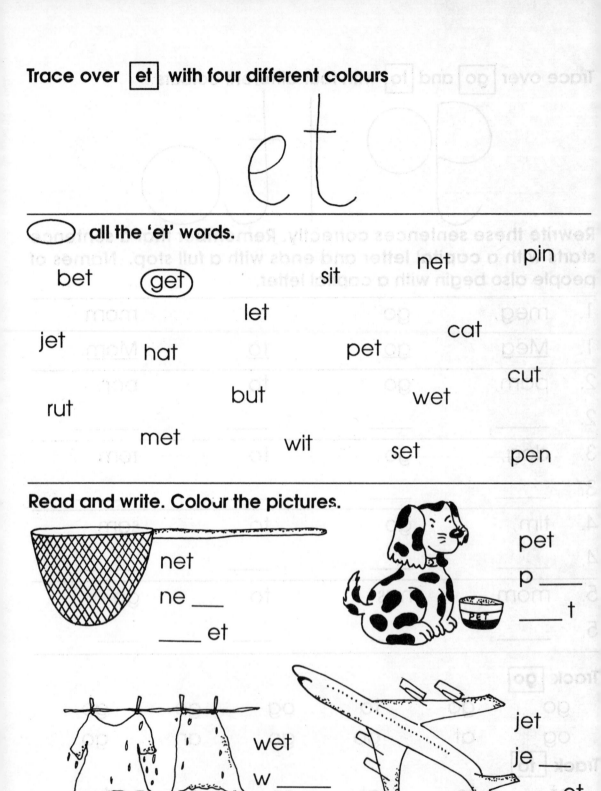

et

◯ **all the 'et' words.**

bet （get） sit net pin

let

jet hat pet cat

rut but wet cut

met wit set pen

Read and write. Colour the pictures.

net

ne ___

___ et

pet

p ___

___ t

wet

w ___

___ t

jet

je ___

___ et

Track et

ot	et	it	am	et	et
et	ut	et	et	at	ot
ef	et	at	it	ut	et
ot	at	et	ut	et	it
el	et	et	at	et	ut

X the odd one out

set	jet	met	man	let	wet
jet	bet	get	wet	wag	set
met	pat	set	net	pet	get
pet	jet	net	let	bet	mat
rat	met	set	net	get	pet

Match the picture to the word and colour the picture

jet

wet

net

pet

55

Trace over these letters with four colours

Fill in the blanks to make 'en' words

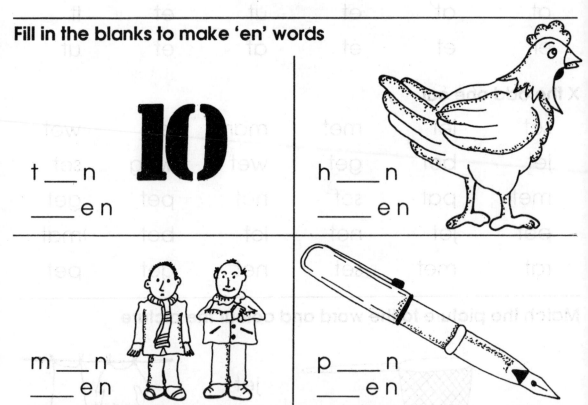

10

t __ n
___ e n

h ___ n
___ e n

m __ n
___ e n

p ___ n
___ e n

⬭ the 'en' words

ten   pen   pat

men   pan

hen   Pam

man

Track [en]

ne	en	et	em	en	en
en	in	en	en	it	am
en	am	in	en	en	at
un	en	ut	en	am	en
in	en	on	at	en	im

Word Search

hen,	pen,	men,	Ben,	den	~~ten~~

a	b	p	e	n	c	d	e
f	g	h	i	d	e	n	j
k	t	e	n	i	m	n	o
p	q	r	s	h	e	n	t
u	v	B	e	n	w	x	y
z	a	b	c	d	m	e	n

Match the picture to the word and colour

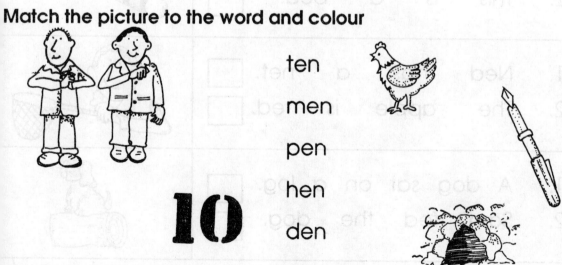

ten

men

pen

hen

den

10

57

Trace over these letters in four colours

Fill in the blanks with 'ed' and read the words.

bed, f_____, l_____,

N____, r_____, T_____,

Read the sentences and ✓ the correct one.

1.	Ted	has	a	hat.	☐
2.	Pam	has	a	fan.	☐

1.	This	is	a	bat.	☐
2.	This	is	a	bed.	☐

1.	Ned	has	a	net.	☐
2.	The	apple	is	red.	☐

1.	A dog sat on a log.	☐
2.	Sam fed the dog.	☐

Track `ed`

ed	et	ed	em	et	ed
de	ed	ed	am	ut	ed
ed	it	ut	ed	ed	at
od	at	ed	un	um	ed
eb	ed	en	et	ed	ed

Read	Spell and circle						Write
bed	d	(b)	i	(e)	b	(d)	bed
fed	t	f	e	a	d	t	
led	l	h	e	u	d	g	
Ned	m	N	i	e	b	d	
red	r	s	a	e	d	p	
Ted	T	B	e	o	g	d	
wed	m	w	u	e	d	y	

◯ all the 'ed' words.

had   nut   lad   Ned

     bad   Ted   wed

bed   red

         did   hid   pad

kid   led   fed

Trace over `eg` **with four different colours**

Make words

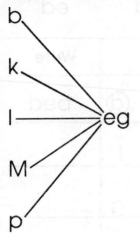

b   beg,   beg

k   k____,   _____

l   eg   l____,   _____

M   M____,   _____

p   p____,   _____

Draw a line from each `peg` **to the picture**

peg   peg   beg   leg

    peg   keg

         peg   peg

peg   beg   peg

      leg

keg   Meg   peg

       peg

Meg   peg

Track eg

eg	at	eg	en	eg	ot
ge	eg	eg	at	in	ug
eg	am	un	eg	im	eg
ug	eg	am	eg	eg	at
eg	ot	ut	in	eg	eg

Match the words and write

beg   Meg   _____

peg   keg   _____

leg   peg   _____

Meg   beg   beg

keg   leg   _____

Name the picture and colour it

leg, peg, Meg

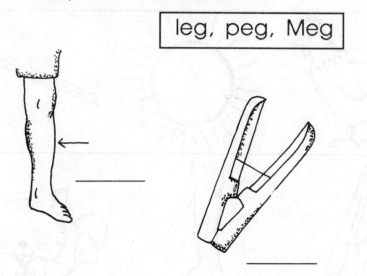

_____   _____

_____

Put them in the right column

| ~~jet~~ den leg red men bed peg pet | | | |
| Ned beg net pen Meg wet ten fed | | | |
et	en	eg	ed
jet			

X the odd one out and colour

et

en

eg

Trace over `the` **with four different colours**

the

Fill in the blanks with `The` **and colour the picture**

_____ sun

_____ van

_____ cat

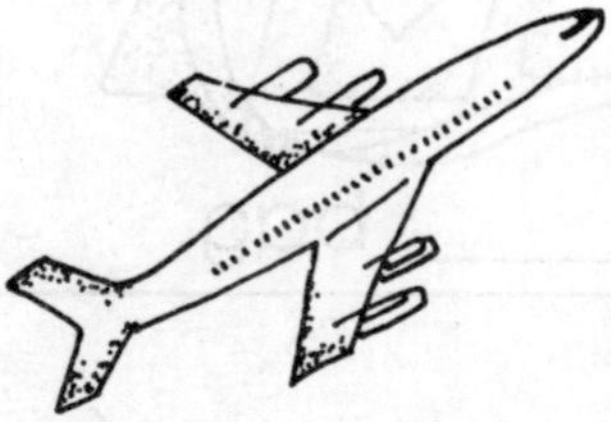

_____ jet

Track `the`

the	her	hen	the	the
hen	hit	the	the	her
the	the	hen	hit	the

Trace over her **with four different colours**

Fill in the blanks with her **and colour the picture**

This   is   Pam.

This   is   ____   pet.

This   is   _____   bag.

This   is   _____   bed.

Giver her a happy face.   Give her a sad face.

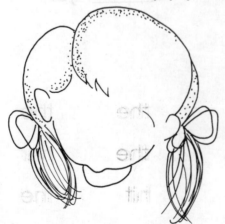   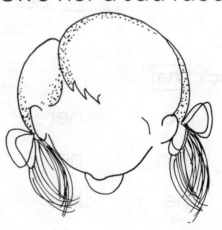

Trace over `here` **with four different colours**

here

Read, copy and colour

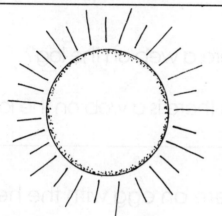

Here is the sun.

_ _ _ _ _ _ _ _ _ _ _ _ _

Here is a bag.

_ _ _ _ _ _ _ _ _ _ _ _ _ _ _

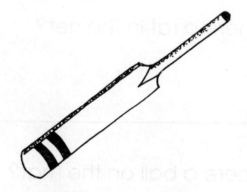

Here is a bat.

_ _ _ _ _ _ _ _ _ _ _ _ _

Here is a cat.

_ _ _ _ _ _ _ _ _ _ _ _ _ _

Trace over there **with four different colours**

there

Read and answer these questions, and colour the pictures

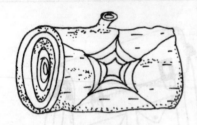

Q.1 Is there a web on the log?

Ans.1 Yes there is a web on the log.

Q2. Is there an egg with the hen?

Ans.2

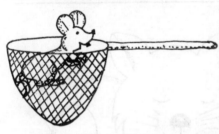

Q3. Is there a rat in the net?

Ans.3

Q4. Is there a ball on the mat?

Ans.4

Trace over ut **with four different colours**

Make words

b.
c. —— ut
g.

but,
c ___,
g ___,

but
___
___

h.
m. —— ut
n.

h ___,
m ___,
n ___,

___
___
___

Read	Spell and circle						Write
but	ⓑ	d	e	ⓤ	f	ⓣ	but
cut	c	r	u	o	t	l	
gut	q	g	u	a	f	t	
hut	h	k	i	u	z	t	
mut	n	m	u	o	t	i	
nut	n	a	e	u	f	t	

⬭ **the twins**

cut	but	nut	but	hut
gut	hut	gut	mut	but
hut	but	gut	hut	nut
cut	mut	nut	hut	cut
nut	gut	nut	cut	hut

Track ☐ut☐

at	ut	ot	at	ut	ut
to	ot	at	ot	ut	ut
tu	at	ut	ut	ot	ut
ut	ut	ot	at	ut	ot
ut	ot	ut	at	ut	it

Read the words in the balls. Colour those parts of the balls that have rhyming words.

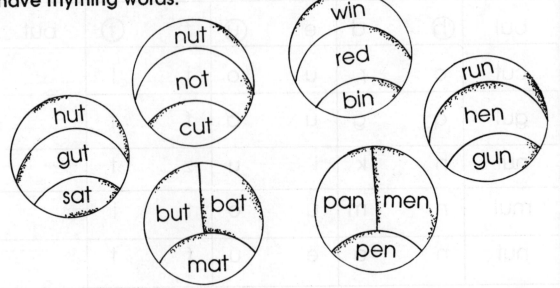

68

Trace over ug **with four different colours**

Fill in the blanks with ug **and read the words**

jug,   b ____,   r ____,

h ____,   d ____,   m ____,

Word Search

~~jug,~~   tug,   rug,   hug, dug,   mug,   bug

a	b	u	g	c	d	e
f	g	h	i	d	u	g
h	u	g	j	k	l	m
n	o	j	u	g	p	q
r	s	t	m	u	g	u
v	t	u	g	w	x	y
z	a	b	c	r	u	g

X the odd one out

tug	rug	rat	mug	hug
bug	bat	hug	tug	rug
mat	mug	rug	dug	bug
bug	rug	sat	tug	mug
bug	mug	dug	rug	hot

Track ug

gu	ug	og	at	ug	in
ug	an	on	ug	ug	ut
eg	up	ug	ug	on	ug
ub	ug	up	ug	ut	ug
ug	at	ug	ug	up	ug

Name the picture and colour it

bug, jug, rug, mug

_____   _____   _____

_____

Trace over un **with four different colours**

un

Make words

f.
r.
s
b
g

un

fun   fun

r ___   ___
s ___   ___
b ___   ___
g ___   ___

Match the column and write

fun	gun	___
run	bun	___
sun	fun	___
bun	run	___
gun	sun	___

Track un

un	an	un	ot	up	un
nu	un	um	an	un	un
an	in	an	un	on	un
um	un	um	un	ut	un
un	an	on	un	un	in

Name the picture and colour it

sun, bun, gun

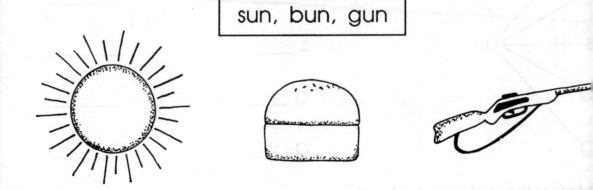

Make new words by changing the vowel

	i	u
f a n	f i n	f u n
b a d		
b a n		
h a t		
b a g		

Trace over `um` **with four different colours**

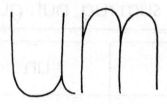

Make words

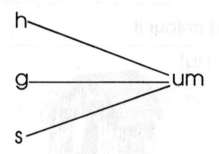

h ——
g ——
s ——

h u m ____
g ____ ____
s ____ ____

Read	Spell and circle						Write
hum	b	(h)	o	(u)	n	(m)	h u m
dum	d	b	u	a	w	m	
gum	p	g	u	e	m	n	
mum	w	m	o	u	m	w	
sum	r	s	u	i	n	m	

Put these words in the right column

jug, but, sun, sum rug, nut, gun, mum

ut	ug	un	um
	jug		

◯ **the name of the picture and colour it**

sum

sun

hut

cut

mug

mut

nut

bug

jug

fun

gun

gum

74

Trace over **put** with four different colours

put

Fill Put in the box. Read and colour

1. [ ] the bat in the bin.

2. [ ] the egg in the cup.

3. [ ] the gun in the box.

4. [ ] the jam on the bun.

Track put

pat	put	pit	put	ptu	put
put	pet	put	pit	put	tup

Trace over but **with four different colours**

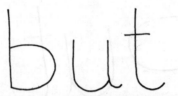

Fill in the blanks

b _ t,   _ u t,   b u ___,

___ t,   b ___,   _ u ___.

Fill in but **in the box. Read and colour**

The cat sat in a hat [   ] the rat sat on a hat.

   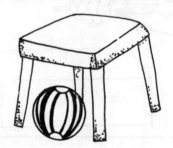

The bat is on the stool [   ] the ball is under the stool.

Track but

but   bat   bet   but   but

bat   but   bit   but   bun

Trace over `you` **with four different colours**

you

Answer the following questions with `Yes` **or** `No`

Q1   Can   you   hop?

Ans. 1   Yes   I   can   hop.

Q2   Have   you   a   dog?

Ans. 2 _

Q3   Can   you   jog?

Ans 3 _

Circle all the 'you's on the yacht

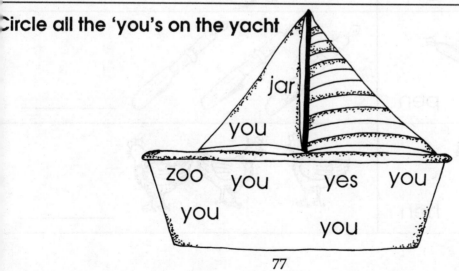

jar

you

zoo   you   yes   you

you

you

77

Make many by adding 's'.

one	many
cat	c a t s
pin	_____
top	_____
gun	_____
pen	_____
hen	_____

Family Fun

Find all the 'an' words and write them in the <u>Can</u>

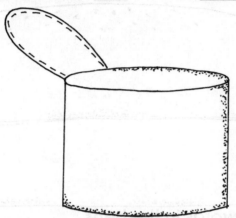

Write all the 'at' words on <u>fat Pat</u>

get	cat	pet	pan	sat	set	can	fat
fan	mat	tan	Pat	man	rat	ran	

Family Fun

Write all the 'un' words in the <u>bun</u>

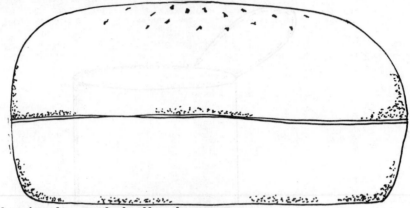

Write all the 'en' words in the <u>hens</u>

Write all the 'og' words in the <u>log</u>

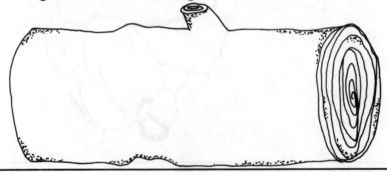

pen	fun	dog	men	sun	jog	ten
log	run	den	gun	fog	nun	